CARTOONS No. 23

from

Evening Standard

and

The Mail

ON SUNDAY

CHAPMANS

1991

Chapmans Publishers Ltd
141–143 Drury Lane
London WC2B 5TB

First published by Chapmans 1991

ISBN 1 85592 715 2

Printed and bound in Great Britain by
Clays Ltd, St Ives plc.

August 1, 1990

One of Britain's most controversial judges, Sir James Miskin, stepped down as Recorder of London, and had some harsh words about the standard of jurors.

"Have the ignoramuses of the jury reached their verdict?"

August 8, 1990

Because of the crisis in the Gulf, Kuwaitis had a £500-a-day limit imposed on their bank accounts — which some found tough to stick to.

"Only £500 a day! Lucky I keep a few million in my Co-op account!"

August 13, 1990

There were fears that Iraq would again resort to chemical weapons.

"Relax guys, it was Shultz's socks again!"

August 14, 1990

During the Gulf crisis British fighter planes flew off to help protect Saudi Arabia from the Iraqis. Meanwhile the drought in Britain continued . . .

"I'm from a desert region myself — North Kent, actually!"

August 21, 1990

As troops poured in to protect Saudi Arabia, the latest children's TV craze in Britain was Teenage Mutant Ninja Turtles.

"Aircraft carriers! Stealth bombers! What are the Americans going to send next?"

August 29, 1990

Ernest Saunders,
former boss of
Guinness, was jailed for
fraud.

August 30, 1990

Millionaire Gerald Ronson, former boss of the Heron group of companies, was jailed for his part in the Guinness fraud case.

"What would you like to drink, Mr Ronson? I'm the wine baron!"

September 3, 1990

American troops were massed in Saudi Arabia and the Gulf, but so far there was still a stand-off with Iraq.

"Only four weeks, sir, and I'm nearly as brown as George Hamilton!"

September 25, 1990

A drugged dart was fired at a race horse during a race, causing jockey Greville Starkey to fall off.

"About half that dose in the next race, Arthur!"

October 1, 1990

Scores of anti-terrorism experts at a conference had a lucky escape when an IRA bomb meant for them was discovered by chance.

"Will the delegate who ate four pounds of what he thought was Shippams's fish paste walk ever so slowly into the main road and await the bomb squad!"

October 4, 1990

Jailed millionaire Gerald Ronson, one of the businessmen convicted in the Guinness fraud trial, claimed he couldn't afford to pay his £5 million fine.

"Don't worry, Gerald, we've already found four and a half million and we haven't even looked in the loft!"

October 7, 1990

The Duke and Duchess of York celebrated moving into their new home with a star-studded house-warming party.

"Let's face it, Percy, we probably weren't invited to Fergie's bash because you can't tell jokes like Billy Connolly!"

October 9, 1990

As British troops massed in the Gulf there were serious problems in transporting all their equipment to them.

"I see the Brits' new camouflage has finally got here!"

October 11, 1990

There were protests after the BBC spent £1,500 on a operation to give former model Cindy Jackson bigger boobs for a feature on the Ruby Wax Show.

"As it's on the BBC, could I have a nose job at the same time?"

October 17, 1990

According to a report on royal spending, the Queen's annual laundry bill was £63,700.

"What with my budget being so tight, and them just standing there doing nothing . . .!"

October 19, 1990

Spanish lorry drivers, furious about soaring fuel prices caused by the Gulf crisis, blockaded roads between France and Spain, leaving imported cargoes to rot.

"I'll tell you who it isn't — it isn't Julio Iglesias!"

October 22, 1990

Education Minister John MacGregor wanted to bring in school testing for seven-year-olds.

"We'll be able to put Rodney down for Eton now he's finally passed his exam for seven-year-olds!"

October 23, 1990

The match between Arsenal and Manchester United ended in a huge brawl on the pitch, in which all the players except the goalies were involved.

"I think I'll give 'Spot the Ball' a miss this week, Vera!"

October 29, 1990

Mrs Thatcher was looking increasingly beleaguered as Tories and the media rounded on her.

"D'you know, darling, I'd got to the last paragraph before I realised they weren't talking about Saddam Hussein!"

October 30, 1990

British Rail said they were introducing on-the-spot fines for fare dodgers.

"Never mind the fine, Arthur, just take his name and address!"

November 4, 1990

Former Prime Minister Edward Heath had successful negotiations in Baghdad with Saddam Hussein for the release of British hostages.

"If you're looking for another dangerous trip, Ted, how about dropping in on the Thatchers?"

November 6, 1990

Michael Heseltine's criticisms of Mrs Thatcher fuelled speculation about a leadership contest.

"They're trying to find someone to stand against her, but nobody's that drunk yet!"

Fergie, on a trip to
Australia, was
embarrassed when a
blast of air made her
skirt fly up.

**"Which one is the
Duchess of York?"**

November 11, 1990

Tony Benn went on a personal mission to Baghdad to try and talk Saddam Hussein into leaving Kuwait and avoiding a war.

"That was the last of the elder statesmen — now for the comedians!"

November 15, 1990

Michael Heseltine launched his challenge against Mrs Thatcher for the Tory leadership.

"What a fantastic day; I've had my hand shaken by Michael Heseltine and kissed Mrs Thatcher, or was it the other way round?"

Deputy Prime Minister Sir Geoffrey Howe launched an astonishing attack on Mrs Thatcher during his resignation speech to the Commons.

"We'd better have something for our nerves, Frank. Could we have four doubles of what Geoffrey Howe had!"

November 22, 1990

Mrs Thatcher resigned.

JAK

"They all wore grey suits!"

November 23, 1990

It was the day after Mrs Thatcher's resignation. How would she spend her time?

"Anyone care to make up a foursome?"

November 29, 1990

John Major may have won the election, but he had been two votes short of an outright victory until his rivals pledged their support for him.

"Let us out! Let us out! We've got to vote for Michael Heseltine!"

The country was still stunned by the circumstances of Mrs Thatcher's departure.

"It was only his lordship's obsessional hatred of Mrs Thatcher that kept him going this long."

December 6, 1990

The Aga Khan pulled out of racing in Britain as a protest about the disqualification of one of his horses.

"The Aga Khan took it with him!"

December 7, 1990

Derbyshire County Council ran short of money. There wasn't enough to fund the County police force.

"A new helmet, Hardcastle! Do you think we're made of money in the Derbyshire police?"

In the scramble for electricity shares the offer was 10 times over-subscribed. The lucky few who got shares stood to make big profits.

"Not a bad day, old boy, got left £118,000,000, but was a bit disappointed with my electricity shares allocation!"

December 13, 1990

Esther Rantzen was behind a national campaign to stop people smacking their children.

"We wouldn't dream of smacking Wayne, we'd sneak up behind him with a twelve-pound sledge hammer!"

December 18, 1990

Polly Peck boss Asil Nadir was arrested on fraud charges, the latest of several financial scandals to hit large companies.

"Algy had money with Barlow Clowes, Freddy with the Levitt Group, and Robin with Polly Peck!"

December 20, 1990

A victim of the recession—Christie's announced drastic redundancy plans.

" . . . finally, Lot 140, an idle half-knackered 19th century porter; now who's start the bidding at a fiver?"

December 21, 1990

Fifteen men in a homosexual vice gang were sentenced at the Old Bailey. The public was agog with newspaper accounts of their bizarre sado-masochistic practices.

"We're the sado-masochist gang. Can we keep our handcuffs on, please?"

December 24, 1990

The craze for the Teenage Mutant Ninja Turtles continued apace.

"We wanted a turkey as usual for Christmas, but the kids are so keen on turtles!"

December 31, 1990

There was some anxiety among army reservists that the military call-up might jeopardise their normal jobs.

"They couldn't send all the Territorials we wanted, sir, would a few aggressive traffic wardens do?"

January 2, 1991

The New Year Honours brought the traditional mixture of surprises and disappointments.

"It's all right Mabel, I think it's a New Year's Honourgram!"

January 4, 1991

Despite our rising telephone bills, British Telecom spent millions on a new corporate image.

"It's a brilliant logo, Wally. Will you take a cheque for 10 million?"

January 10, 1991

Graham Partridge, a 75-year-old farmer, returned home at dawn to find his house had been ransacked by 27-year-old trainee solicitor Kathryn George-Harries, who called herself his Number One Tart.

"... and your lawyer called!"

January 15, 1991

As war loomed, every newspaper seemed to boast its own battle plan.

"Well, I think they're going to use the Sunday Sport plan!"

January 17, 1991

Overnight the first
bombing raids on
Baghdad had started.
The battle to liberate
Kuwait was on.

Now it begins

"Why aren't you out
fighting in the Gulf?"

January 21, 1991

Allied bombing raids
were flattening
Baghdad.

"They've moved in
fast!"

January 22, 1991

Having been first with the news of the Gulf War, CNN were enjoying rush of new customers.

JAK

"It's all right; he's from Cable News Network!"

January 25, 1991

Americans were keeping away from England because of fears of terrorist reprisals over the Gulf War.

"Of course we're waiting for him: he's our only passenger!"

January 28, 1991

The Allies in the Gulf War were using carpet bombing on Saddam's ground army.

"You know if it wasn't for Vera Lynn every night, I think I'd crack up!"

February 1, 1991

Nervous US holidaymakers were keeping well away from Britain.

"To Elmer J. Hackenbecker, the only American to fly to London since the Gulf war . . . "

The Government decided to award an immediate 12 per cent pay increase to the Army.

"I'm sure your pay increase must be in the post, Arthur!"

February 6, 1991

The first snows of the British winter were sweeping in from Scandinavia as weathermen warned of temperatures of minus 10.

"If it's 20 below for more than 10 consecutive days, nip up to the village, get a Form B7176/H from the Post Office, fill it in with certificate 667811 from the DSS, and you can claim a gallon of paraffin for your heater!"

February 7, 1991

Restaurants were in crisis as the recession and the threat of Gulf War terrorism kept tourists away from Britain. In London nearly a restaurant a day was going out of business.

"I say, isn't that the famous chef who threw us out the other night for asking for a steak well done?"

February 10, 1991

As more and more British troops were moved to the Gulf there was some sensitivity about any Jewish connections.

"As we suspected, another St Michael's label."

February 14, 1991

During the cold snap a plumber charged £150 for a few minutes' work fixing a burst pipe.

"All right, my eldest daughter and Rembrandt — now will you fix the plumbing?"

February 21, 1991

For the second day running, hundreds of Underground passengers were trapped on the Central Line for six hours after smoke was seen billowing from a train.

"This ticket is three days out of date!"

February 27, 1991

Sankyo Seika, one of Japan's largest textiles firms, paid £65 million for the DAKS Simpson clothing company.

"Old Bertie's been buying his suits from Simpson's for years!"

March 1, 1991

Months after being forced out by Saddam Hussein, British diplomats returned to their embassy in Kuwait.

"By Jove Carruthers, haven't our cucumbers done well!"

March 5, 1991

The Bishop of Durham said we should not hold a victory parade for the British soldiers back from the Gulf War.

"I think it's the Bishop of Durham's victory parade!"

March 6, 1991

The Queen needed stitches after being bitten by a corgi when she tried to break up a fight between the roya[l] dogs.

"Which was the one tha[t] bit you, Mummy?"

March 7, 1991

A milkman raised the alarm after hearing the anguished cries of a millionaire's wife who had been held to ransom for five days.

"One bottle or two?"

March 10, 1991

Patients tired of Britain's long hospital waiting lists were travelling to France for their operations.

"Alors, the operation was a complete success, but the hospital food was too rich for him!"

March 12, 1991

There was an outcry over artificial insemination when three women wanted to have babies but not sex. Without a parental relationship behind the birth, said opponents, it was like buying a can of beans.

"I got Arthur at Sainsbury's, but I think he's past his sell-by date!"

March 17, 1991

At the appeal hearing for the Birmingham Si at the Old Bailey, 14 officers of the West Midlands police were described as "liars" or "unreliable".

"Is it worth the risk, dear? Why don't we go to Windsor Safari Park instead?"

March 21, 1991

In the Budget, Chancellor Norman Lamont introduced a £200 tax on car 'phones, which he described as one of the curses of our times.

"I'm afraid you'll have to go, Fiona. I just couldn't live without a car phone."

March 22, 1991

New Zealand horsewoman Heather Tonkin claimed Capt Mark Phillips was the father of her five-year-old daughter Felicity.

"Yes, he is available for stud work and for £3,00 we'll throw in a horse!'

March 27, 1991

A woman and her lover were convicted of plotting to murder the woman's husband by faking a lawnmower accident.

"I can't think why, but Kevin thinks it's safer that way!"

April 2, 1991

It was the first week of the biggest reorganisation of the health service since the NHS began . . . and thousands more administrators were needed.

"I'm sorry, we're all administrators, but I'm sure there'll be a doctor along in a minute!"

April 3, 1991

Former footballer and TV sports presenter David Icke held a press conference to warn about a series of disasters he foresaw for the world. He said he "channelled an energy known as the Christ spirit". And he had also heard from Socrates . . .

"...however, on the good side, David Icke says he can see the end of the recession!"

April 4, 1991

Elton John dressed in drag to perform in one of Rod Stewart's Wembley concerts.

"Has anybody ever told you, you look like Elton John?"

April 9, 1991

London Zoo, long beset by financial problems, announced it was going to close.

"Wasn't this where London Zoo used to be?"

April 10, 1991

A Consumers Association report said there was no evidence of royal jelly having health-giving properties. You might as well eat corn flakes, they said.

"Of course, you can't spread dried rhino-dung on your toast as you can **Royal Jelly!**"

April 11, 1991

Firms who used humour to get round rules against sexist advertising were heavily criticised by the Advertising Standards Authority. They included a company which used the line, "Last time we ran an ad for Swedish lingerie 78 women complained. No men."

"Apparently it's got 100 per cent approval of the Advertising Standards Authority!"

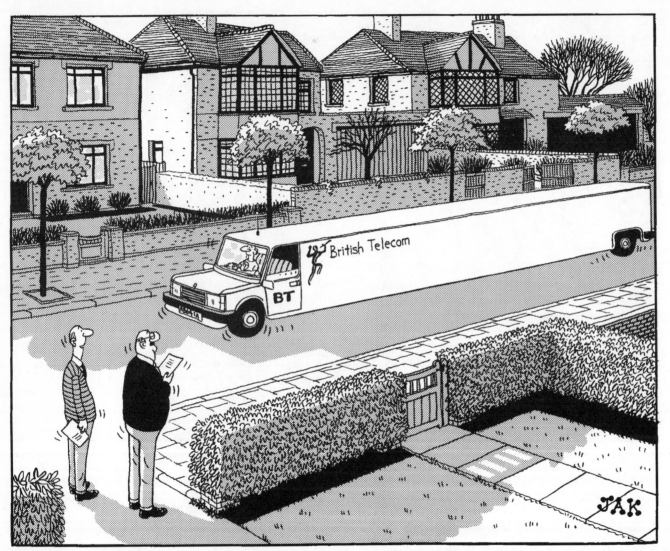

April 12, 1991

British Telecom admitted it had been charging customers th new 17½ per cent VAT for months before the rate officially started.

"I think it's what they deliver the VAT bills in!"

April 15, 1991

According to the News of the World, while Chancellor Norman Lamont was living at 11 Downing Street, his home was being rented by sex therapist Sara Dale, charging £90 a go for lessons in sado masochism in Mr Lamont's basement.

"Just tell him it's the Chief Whip with a complaint about the rent!"

April 18, 1991

Labour's plan for government in the Nineties included a "thrift tax" on savers.

". . . and that red button puts all the money in Switzerland if Labour gets in!"

April 21, 1991

As a replacement for the poll tax a new system of grading houses on size and amenities was announced by the Government. Would a little thing like the London Marathon put off the grading inspectors?

"But surely you can remember if your kitchen is more than 6ft by 6ft?"

April 28, 1991

British Rail was running a campaign to smarten up its employees.

"Pity old Percy's a bit too far gone for Savile Row suits, so we may have to put him down!"

April 29, 1991

H E Bates's 'Darling Buds' book was a huge TV hit, but Pop Larkin's character in the series, gloriously happy and unfettered by income tax, was an unlikely hero to some . . .

"Yes, we've all seen 'The Darling Buds of May', Mr Larkin, and frankly you've become something of an embarrassment to the Inland Revenue!"

May 2, 1991

The Commons tried to force through a bill to allow the presecution of Nazi criminals living in this country, despite the Lords' efforts to block it.

"Ve will haff to make ein run for it!"

May 3, 1991

A ballot of MCC members voted overwhelmingly against admitting women.

"Damned if I know, Ponsonby, none of us could tell boys from gels at Eton!"

May 5, 1991

Sunday trading laws were branded "virtually unenforceable" after two major chain stores won a legal victory allowing them to open seven days a week.

"And lastly I come to the shameful and heretical business of Sunday trading!"

May 7, 1991

America had an attack of the jitters when President Bush was admitted to hospital after suffering irregular heart rhythms. Would Dan Quayle really be in charge?

"Don't worry Dan, if anything important comes up, I'll handle it!"

May 9, 1991

During their claim for unfair dismissal, butler Patrick Davison and his wife Patricia told an industrial tribunal that Mrs Davison's successor as cook tipped a £500 bottle of Chateau Lafite into the goulash.

"The service has improved since they went to the industrial tribunal, and just wait till you taste the cooking!"

May 10, 1991

Scientists announced a breakthrough that would let them decide the sex of babies.

"We couldn't afford a complete gene change for Arthur!"

May 15, 1991

Madonna was stealing the limelight at the Cannes Film Festival.

"My wife buys her corsets from the same shop!"

May 30, 1991

There was an outcry about substantial pay rises for City mandarins. Then Rolls-Royce's boss accepted a cut because his company had not performed as well as he had hoped.

"Bloody scab!"

May 31, 1991

After a series of horrific attacks on humans by so-called danger dogs, the Government warned it might have up to 10,000 animals destroyed.

"I had to have my pit bull put down, but I'm hoping to breed from him if I can find the right sort of girl!"

June 3, 1991

The film Silence of the Lambs, starring Anthony Hopkins as the psychotic killer Dr Hannibal Lecter, was terrifying cinema audiences throughout the country.

"My waiting list has been cut down dramatically since I changed my name to Hannibal!"

June 4, 1991

Banks were accused of increasing their profit margins on loans to small businesses, many of which were going out of business during the recession.

"Regarding the outstanding debt on your small business loan, it's not strictly true that the bank can't get its pound of flesh!"

Prince William had to undergo an exploratory operation after an inexpertly aimed golf club at his prep school chipped part of his skull.

"We're doing everything we can with the guilty boy. There's a top professional from Wentworth working on his swing!"

June 6, 1991

Hollywood came to Yorkshire when Raquel Welch's son married the daughter of former cricketer Fred Trueman. After their American wedding ceremony there was a service of blessing at Bolton Abbey.

"Ee bah gum! Do you expect me to believe you've been out all night with Raquel Welch?"

June 7, 1991

During a row involving one of his neighbours, advertising boss Charles Saatchi's green Rolls-Royce was damaged by fire.

"Will you be requiring the car tonight Mr Saatchi?"

June 12, 1991

Violinist Nigel Kennedy was attacked for his eccentric dress sense by Radio Three controller John Drummond.

"And quite frankly, Nigel, I don't think you backing group goes with Brahms either!"

June 13, 1991

The Thatcher-inspired Bruges Group of MPs were giving John Major more headaches by not backing the Tories' pro-European stance.

"By the way, John, what are you going to do with the Bruges Group?"

London Zoo was being forced to close becaus of money troubles.

"I know the zoo's closing, darling, but why couldn't you bring back a gerbil like the neighbours?"

June 16, 1991

A married naval officer and a Wren from the same crew were court martialled after being found in bed together on board ship.

"Welcome aboard, Miller. I think you'll find this a happy ship!"

June 18, 1991

French Prime Minister Edith Cresson claimed that one in four Englishmen were homosexual because when she walked along the street she didn't feel their eyes on her.

"**Madame le Premiere Ministre, c'est l'ambassadeur de Grande Bretagne, avec une fres forte 'complaint' contre vous!**"

June 19, 1991

Lloyd's underwriters, worried about their massive financial losses, asked to be bailed out by the government.

"I gather some of the 'Names' still think they're getting their money back!"

Prince Charles was
suffering from chronic
back pain and was told
he would have to give
up his actionman
lifestyle.

"Another bottle of
Sloan's horse liniment
Your Royal Highness?

June 21, 1991

There was a huge march through the City of London to celebrate the allied forces' Gulf War victory.

"Why don't you have a goat for a mascot like other regiments?"

June 24, 1991

John Major was said to feel "stabbed in the back" by Mrs Thatcher's anti-European speech in America.

"Honestly Margaret, it's one of the very finest sheltered old people's homes!"

June 25, 1991

Torrential rain washed out Wimbledon.

"Put your money away Gertie: he's not a ticket tout!"

June 26, 1991

Strawberries were being challenged as the traditional, if pricy, fare for the Wimbledon crowds. Bananas were coming up on the outside . . .

"Same as the strawberries, sir, eight quid a bowl!

June 27, 1991

Questions were asked in the Commons after National Power's chief executive John Baker was given a 58 per cent pay rise.

"Well Jackson, it had been the board's intention to give you a 58 per cent rise, but with all the fuss . . . !"

June 30, 1991

Rain disrupted the Wimbledon timetable so badly that for the first time matches were played on a Sunday.

"Speed it up, you lot — there's a big backlog to catch up on!"

July 1, 1991

There was controversy over whether the Queen should pay tax, and HRH said she might have to sell Windsor Castle if the tax changes were made.

"Had it been in the family very long?

July 4, 1991

England was enduring the dullest summer for decades, but the weather was still better than Scotland's.

"There's one of those new English Tourist Board posters!"

July 7, 1991

American tennis player Andre Agassi was the new hit of Wimbledon.

"Come now, Madam, with a little imagination you could hardly tell them apart!"

July 8, 1991

Minister of Defence Tom King warned of massive cuts in militar spending.

"We found it was the horses that were costing the money!"

July 9, 1991

The leader of Abu Dhabi, Sheikh Zayed bin Sultan al-Nahyan, lost £1 billion when Bank of England officials froze the funds of the Bank of Credit and Commerce International because of irregularities.

"I can assure you Sheikh, I only joined the bank from Barclays last week!"

July 10, 1991

Two remand prisoners charged with terrorist offences escaped from Brixton Prison using a gun which had been hidden in a training shoe.

"On the other hand, he could be a Freemason!"

July 11, 1991

Massive cuts in the size of the army were announced by Tom King, the Minister of Defence.

JAK

"... and now to the rousing tune of The British Grenadiers, the massed bands of the Brigade of Guards ..."

July 12, 1991

Ever sterner warnings were being issued on cigarette packets.

"I've only got a death warning in my packet!"

July 14, 1991

The benefactors of the National Gallery's new wing were Sainsbury's, the supermarket owners.

"I've been going round for hours but I still can't find the chicken tikka anywhere!"

July 16, 1991

Western Isles Council in Scotland lost £23 million in the BCCI bank collapse.

"It's another local council treasurer, Hamish, and the worst case of suicide so far!"

July 17, 1991

Is nothing secret? MI5's security was looking shaky when their banking arrangements became public.

"MI5 deposit account? Down six floors and second sliding steel door on your right!"

August 2, 1991

The Duchess of York was shedding weight at a £1000-a-day health farm in Surrey.

"They're doing wonders with Fergie's thighs!"

August 6, 1991

A new report showed that serious complaints about British Rail had soared by 200 per cent over the previous 12 months.

"Apparently it's a hoax, but they can't find the staff to take it down!"

August 7, 1991

Despite Special Branch warnings that a jailbreak was being planned, IRA suspects Nessan Quinlan and Pearce McAley still managed to escape from Brixton Prison, causing one of the most embarrassing security fiascos Britain has ever faced.

"You could only see a jailbreak like this at Brixton!"

August 8, 1991

There was mounting criticism that not all the people asking for handouts on the street were in fact needy cases.

"Come on Sid! It's your turn to go begging!"

August 9, 1991

The Prince and Princess of Wales, on holiday in Spain, were again being mercilessly pestered by photographers.

"Just one more on F16 at five hundredths of a second!"

August 12, 1991

New rules were
introduced to force
owners to muzzle
so-called danger dogs
when they were in
public places.

"Here's another one
who didn't read the new
regulations properly!"

August 15, 1991

The Inland Revenue launched a campaign give itself a friendlier image.

"I'm afraid there's nothing we can do for Johnson, he's been in the job too long!"

August 22, 1991

The Soviet coup leaders who temporarily overthrew Mikhail Gorbachev had claimed that ill health had made him unfit to rule the USSR.

JAK

"If I'd known what a sick lot you were, I'd never have started it!"

August 23, 1991

Mikhail Gorbachev wa
deposed while he was
on holiday in the
Crimea, only to be
returned to the
Kremlin after a matter
of hours.

"... and this is where
Mikhail gets seized by
the KGB!"